CONTENTS

The Fireside Book

A picture and a poem for every mood
chosen by

David Hope

Printed and published by D.C. THOMSON & CO., LTD.,
185 Fleet Street, LONDON EC4A 2HS. © D.C. Thomson & Co., Ltd., 2008

GARDEN PARTY

BRIGHT-EYED, upon the weighted, leaning fence,
  Birds formed an anxious bread-line in the snow
That pressed upon the frosted Winter earth
And stifled dormant sustenance below.
Silence and hunger stalked the Winter day —
Till casements creaked and opened overhead.
Hands filled with morning promise braved the sill
And like a benediction, scattered bread.

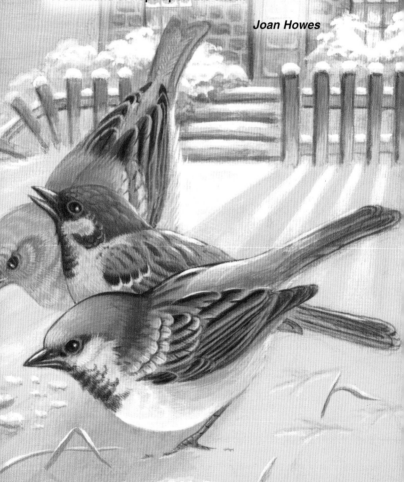

Sparrows, as dried and brown as fallen leaves,
Came first to taste the banquet — and their ease
Dared chaffinches, with dawn upon their breasts,
To timidly vacate the spangled trees.
Gaily, the breakfast party took their fill —
A tiny pageant on the lawn below.
Weaving with matchstick grace and fragile joy,
A saraband of hope upon the snow.

Joan Howes

NATURE'S CHILD

OH little child of hoary frost,
    That, by chance, has nature tossed
With icy hands in wood and lane,
To make our spirits soar again;
God blessed the ground in which you grow
That gives you birth in virgin snow,
What would life be, no-one can tell,
Without a snowdrop in the dell . . .

Brian H. Gent

REDBREAST

EIGHT below and I go out to give you crumbs
   On the slab of wood that serves as a bird table.
I know you're a thug really; you chase the other birds
away
And battle tooth and nail with all the other robins —
Yet I can't help marvelling at your startling orange breast
There on a Winter's day, unafraid of the heavy thud
   of my boots.
You even come to my hand to eat, all however many
   grams of you —
There, trusting, in the very heart of my palm.
So, eight below on a dark December day
I still go out to give you crumbs, and wait for you to land
Soft as a moth, eyes bright chinks, your breast beating
Before nightfall swallows us all.

Kenneth C. Steven

GREEN

SUDDENLY green is in,
skirts, dresses, smocks,
suits, shirts, socks and hats,
green is the passionate fashion.

Everything is greening up,
field, flower, hedge and crown,
power packed in explosive quiet,
bursting in a riotous, luscious rush.

Enviable burgeoning green,
unfurling, twirling, twisting,
curling, reaching, unravelling,
wreathing and pleaching purl and plain.

Shining green entwined
with sunlight, patulous malachite,
beryl and lime, celadon and straddling
jade; Spring's splendid, pendulous parade.

John Ellis

FLAME

IT hardly seemed worth all the trouble then,
  clearing out the ash, tearing up paper,
setting sticks and coal, just to make a fire
when I was only passing through, one bright

April afternoon, pausing to enjoy tea,
a snooze, a book, sitting in the sun.
But, once the flame took hold, coaxed by orange peel
and a firelighter, I was glad to see

how bright the dimly-lit room had become,
and the daffodils that I had planted
by "my" roadside ducked and nodded their heads.
I stared at the trees ready to explode

with green, then curled up with my paperback
and read about Melchester with its long
low-hipped roofs, and heard the branches scratching
at my window pane. I stoked the fire once

more before I left, watched the smoke rise up
from the twin chimneys like grey stockinged legs,
and saw the fire burn brightly through the glass,
knowing that it would be gone, when I returned.

Ruth M. L. Walker

TO A SPRING WIND

FROM aerie berths where wind is born
  and chooses fate as breeze or storm,
a gust of Spring appears inclined
to thaw each wintry nook it finds
and of long, golden hours warn.

My empty currant bushes bow,
and frilly cedars wonder how
this little messenger of Spring,
so certain of the news it brings,
can manage Mother Nature's vow.

Buoyant with a sprightly glee,
the gust awakens bud and tree;
and all aglow with green's first kiss,
my yard, unable to resist,
yields to Spring's sweet bribery.

Rachel Wallace-Oberle

THE CUCKOO

I HEARD the cuckoo call,
  cycling back along the secret ways
of rural Worcestershire.
It was that special time of year
when early Spring, ablaze,
holds the waiting world in thrall.

Across the meadows' sprawl
her dual notes, soft-stressed,
filled the afternoon,
enchanting it. I wondered then,
that mid-March day, was I the first
to hear the cuckoo call?

John Ellis

A CAT CALLED TEA BAG

A CAT called Tea Bag has to be
   An asset to society.
Endowed with every social grace,
The friendly paw, the kindly face.
A cat hospitable and kind
Whose guests will instantly unwind
When offered, as their host appears,
Large measures of the cup that cheers:
Tea Bag is careful with his dress,
A sure sartorial success.
A cat who always gets it right,
Properly clad in black and white.

Joan Howes

APPLE TREE DREAMS

WHAT better place to sit and dream
than 'neath an apple tree,
entranced by nodding branches and
the hum of passing bee,
a place of drifting blossom in the
scented Springtime days,
where buds are blessed by showers
and the sunlight's golden rays,
where apples swell and ripen as the
seasons dawdle by,
to reach a sweet fruition when the
Autumn days draw nigh.
This world's so full of wonders that
an apple tree seems small,
but still I think such simple joys
may yet be best of all.

Margaret Ingall

WOODLARKS

SECRETIVE and hidden
In the undergrowth
Of wooded heath,
A compact cup of nest
Pulses four gaping beaks,
Upping periscope,
When the parent birds
Arrive, unload hampers
Of insect and seed.

Soon they will learn
To fly skywards,
Spiralling up to become
Lost little pin pricks
In the deep cerulean sky,
Before reaching their zenith
And abseiling their descent,
Slow, slow, easy does it —
Back to Mother Earth.

David Elder

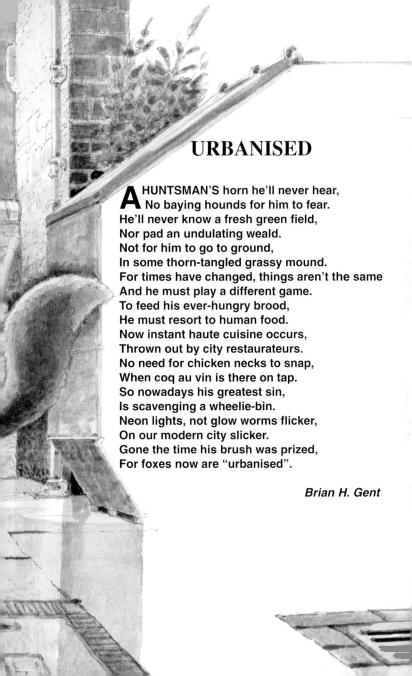

URBANISED

A HUNTSMAN'S horn he'll never hear,
  No baying hounds for him to fear.
He'll never know a fresh green field,
Nor pad an undulating weald.
Not for him to go to ground,
In some thorn-tangled grassy mound.
For times have changed, things aren't the same
And he must play a different game.
To feed his ever-hungry brood,
He must resort to human food.
Now instant haute cuisine occurs,
Thrown out by city restaurateurs.
No need for chicken necks to snap,
When coq au vin is there on tap.
So nowadays his greatest sin,
Is scavenging a wheelie-bin.
Neon lights, not glow worms flicker,
On our modern city slicker.
Gone the time his brush was prized,
For foxes now are "urbanised".

Brian H. Gent

A DAY IN APRIL

TWELVE o'clock. She stands in the back porch,
Strands of gold hair tangling her face.
She calls his name; her voice is blown away.
He looks up nonetheless, as though he's heard
Somewhere deep inside. Light scours the hills,
Gullies of wind sweep back the shadow.
Fleet's heard her, flows down the field
In a bouncing waterfall of black and white.
She smiles. A lamb pities the air
With a cry as thin as milk. She turns inside.

He thuds the mud from his boots.
Has the mail come? Delivery from Hulberts?
The clock flickers softly in the hall;
Up in the landing window the blue of April
A rippling flag of sky —
This land is in his hands
As surely as it ran his father's.
At the table she rumbles the potatoes from the pan,
Looks at him with soft eyes. I've good news, she murmurs.

Kenneth C. Steven

THE HORSE ON THE HILL

CARVED in chalk, he stands there,
The white horse on the hill,
And no-one knows who made him,
And maybe never will.
His hooves are poised, impatient,
Each sinew strains to fly,
Yet still the hillside holds him
As centuries slip by.
Perhaps one stormy midnight
When rain has soaked the earth,
He'll break his grassy fetters,
He'll stamp the sodden turf,
And in a flash of lightning,
One crashing thund'rous blast,
He'll raise his head and whinny
And gallop free at last.

Margaret Ingall

SUMMER LIGHTNING

THE giant cloud clears its throat,
   a hangover cold from May;
like an old photograph the sky,
all colour faded,
is etched in sepia grey.

The heavens rumble, escalating thunder,
the crows in field take flight;
the downpour begins,
rain hums a beat
to the flashes of strobe-white light.

David Elder

SWEET SCENT OF TWILIGHT

SWEET scent of twilight fills the air,
Tranquillity is everywhere.
Hedgehogs sniff the evening breeze
And little moles in burrows squeeze.
Owls and bats have taken flight,
To disappear into the night.
With magical and wondrous scales,
Bestowed by little nightingales.
What a privilege it is to share,
The scent of twilight in the air.

Brian H. Gent

A SUMMER DAY

TAKE time to dream, and rest awhile
   by curving brook, where willows trail
their lacy fronds at water's edge,
where reeds grow tall, to cast a shade,
o'er sun-filled hours of Summer's day,
and fragrance of the balmy air,
is caught upon the cooling breeze.

Take time to view the spreading hills,
whose distance lends enchanting scenes,
to take the mind down memory lane,
when taking time to dream a dream . . .

Elizabeth Gozney

HAREBELL

WIND blows savagely across moor
and thickset heather
Making little impression.
A lonely harebell
Bows and scrapes
Twisting this way and that
At the mercy of its tormentor.
Such fragile beauty
Deceptively strong.
The wind dies away
Defeated.

Heather Innes

SUMMER'S MUSIC HALL

WHEN dawn draws back night's curtain
In Summer's music hall,
A verdant stage is ringing
With blackbird's fluting call.

The spotlight in the heavens
Shines down, and in its beams
It catches scenes revealing
Performers of sweet themes.

Whilst warblers join the choir
Of finches in fine song,
Plump bees and cooling breezes
Hum pleasantly along.

The gallery is crowded
With gnats and humble flies,
And, in the stalls, wee daisies
Look up with dewy eyes.

And through the long, warm hours,
Until the eventide,
The songsters' voices echo
Across the countryside.

Alice Jean Don

SWEET WILLIAM

DEAR William is rather more
   Than most cat owners bargain for!
An ample person, kind of face,
With all the customary grace
Of felines, be they large or small,
Nature's balletic ones withal!

Where lesser cats are lean as pipes,
Dear William favours downward stripes
That smooth his figure to a "T"
And match his quiet dignity.
A cat proved elegant and wise —
By dressing down, to suit his size!

Joan Howes

BRIAR ROSES
ON THE PATH

I FOUND while I was walking through
an isle of pine and fragile fern,
a path, forsaken, yielding to
an aimless sort of wistful turn
as if unable to discern
exactly what it ought to do.

I thought this place apart morose
— a promise pierced with emptiness —
and then I saw the briar rose,
tumultuous upon the crest,
sacrificing loveliness
on a path where no one goes.

Rachel Wallace-Oberle

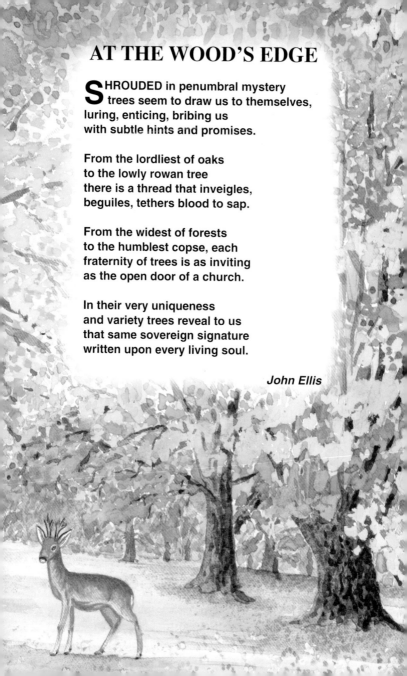

AT THE WOOD'S EDGE

SHROUDED in penumbral mystery
trees seem to draw us to themselves,
luring, enticing, bribing us
with subtle hints and promises.

From the lordliest of oaks
to the lowly rowan tree
there is a thread that inveigles,
beguiles, tethers blood to sap.

From the widest of forests
to the humblest copse, each
fraternity of trees is as inviting
as the open door of a church.

In their very uniqueness
and variety trees reveal to us
that same sovereign signature
written upon every living soul.

John Ellis

HARBOUR SCENE

THE sun spreads out a cloth of gold
  Across the morning sky,
The world shakes off the shrouds of sleep
Awakening with a sigh.
A million dancing dazzling lights
Are bouncing off the sea,
And overhead gulls are soaring
Winging wild and free.

The gentle lapping of the waves
'Gainst boats moored in the bay,
And shells are scattered on the sand —
There's salty tang of spray.
Seaweed tangled in old ropes
The sound of creaking crafts,
The harbour life a busy scene
Of vessels, sails and masts.

And old men mending fishing nets
Are sitting by the quay.
Their wrinkled faces weathered brown
Just gazing out to sea.
Their eyes scan the horizon far
Until at last they've spied,
The fishing boats all coming home
With turning of the tide.

Kathleen Gillum

GLOWING SEASCAPE

THE moon crept away through the Heavens.
The sea crept away from the sand,
And while all the world was still sleeping,
New dawning crept over the land.

The silvery hue from the zenith
Was caught on the waves in their ebb,
Like soft gauzy wings of an insect
Entrapped in a finely spun web.

Tranquillity lay on the coastline.
Serenity rode on the flow,
And, visible over the seascape,
A breathtaking, magical glow.

Alice Jean Don

WHERE MINNOWS SWIM

TAKE me please where minnows swim
 And dragonflies the waters skim,
Where obese toads survey the scene
And ducklings virgin feathers preen;
Where stately iris, purest white
Shimmer in the sun's bright light,
With stepping stones, green mossy clad,
That jostle with the lily pad.
Where could there be a better place,
To sit beneath a willow's grace,
Or stroll beside the grass-edged rim,
And watch the little minnows swim.

Brian H. Gent

SUMMER HEALING

GREEN reflection on the water,
Shadowed green beneath the trees,
Summer filling field and meadow
Summer fragrance on the breeze.
Green beside the lake and river,
Waterfall and flowing stream,
Peaceful thoughts and quiet moments
Nourishing each Summer dream.

In the town and city gardens
Beauty there for all to see,
Green in bushes and in hedges
And in every leafy tree.
Green the path along the hillside
Where the distant mountain rolls,
Summer gifts and Summer blessings
Touching hearts and healing souls.

Iris Hesselden

SEA CHANGE

SMALL sunbrowned feet,
  marking a memory
on warm, wet sand.
The thin flutes of children's laughter
Above the shoosh and recede
Of toe-tickling breakers.
"Let's make a moat" comes the cry —
And the willing feet earnestly plod
Back and forth with buckets
To the obliging waves.
All is joy and innocent delight
In the bounty of shells and bladderwrack
Gathered to festoon their lop-sided ramparts.
A camera clicks —
The ozone moment is held fast,
To be treasured among the poignant sea-spray
Of recollected childhood.

Joan Howes

LIKE A PICTURE BOOK

OH bright flaming sun you have lured me today
 To find grassy banks where the wild flowers sway;
Where mallard ducks swim on the river's clear flow,
(Proud parents of curious ducklings in tow);
Where butterflies dance, and the swallows in flight
Swoop down for the catch of the midges in sight.

You've lured me when noon-time slips drowsily by,
And clouds are far flung in a sapphire-blue sky;
When blossom is hiding a nest in the bush,
A home which, in bird-world, must surely seem lush;
When Nature has made everywhere that I look,
As lovely as scenes in a child's picture book.

Alice Jean Don.

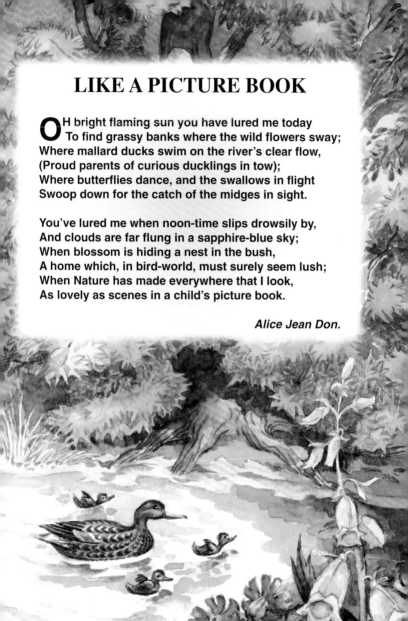

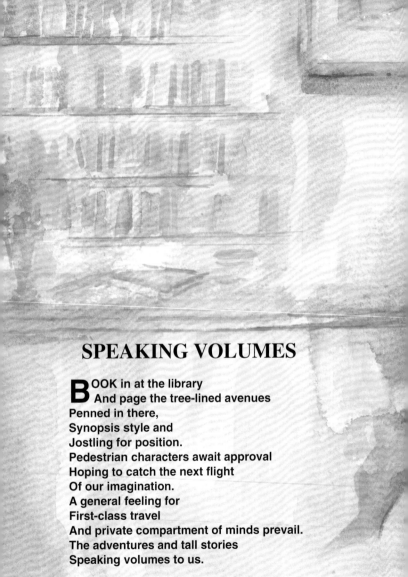

SPEAKING VOLUMES

BOOK in at the library
And page the tree-lined avenues
Penned in there,
Synopsis style and
Jostling for position.
Pedestrian characters await approval
Hoping to catch the next flight
Of our imagination.
A general feeling for
First-class travel
And private compartment of minds prevail.
The adventures and tall stories
Speaking volumes to us.

Dorothy McGregor

CATERPILLARS

GREEN caterpillars waxing fat,
In brassicas' sweet habitat,
Tightly cling tenacious feet,
In their shady leaved retreat,
How happily they munch away,
From dawn until the sun's last ray,
And then, to end their life of bliss,
Each one becomes a chrysalis;
That's when they cast their magic spell,
Just how they do it who can tell,
With nothing hidden up their sleeve,
The trick they pull you'd scarce believe,
But there, before your very eyes,
Hey Presto! They are butterflies!

Brian H. Gent

PEACEFUL
RENDEZVOUS

THE moon in starry heavens,
Her flaxen wings far spanned,
Presided o'er the meeting
Of sea and dreamy land.
Her splendid quiet powers,
Like magic filtered through,
Romantically endorsing
A peaceful rendezvous.

She reached into the waters
That shimmered radiantly,
And showed the nicer nature
Of deep, mysterious sea —
An ocean softly whisp'ring
The lyrics of its tide,
As though it spoke to angels
On calm land sanctified.

Alice Jean Don

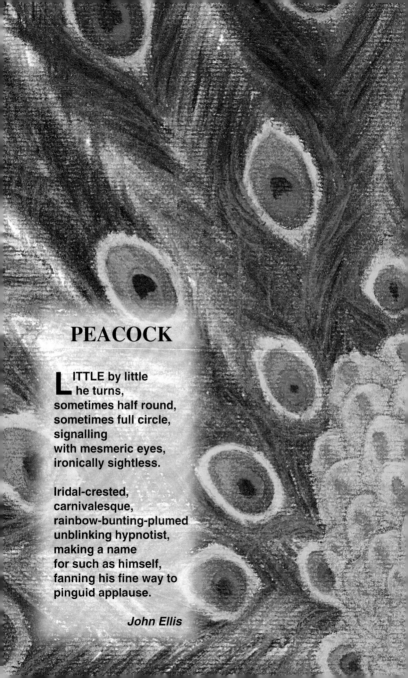

PEACOCK

LITTLE by little
he turns,
sometimes half round,
sometimes full circle,
signalling
with mesmeric eyes,
ironically sightless.

Iridal-crested,
carnivalesque,
rainbow-bunting-plumed
unblinking hypnotist,
making a name
for such as himself,
fanning his fine way to
pinguid applause.

John Ellis

NATURE'S PARADISE

SOFT against the garden wall,
Buddleia's arching branches fall,
As dappled verdant leaves cascade,
Creating breathless Summer shade,
And so the magic spell is cast,
Providing Nature's sweet repast,
Where flowers butterflies entice,
In purpled, perfumed paradise . . .

Brian H. Gent

MIDNIGHT TRAVELLER

FULL moon, and by the shadowed verge,
Half camouflaged from sight,
The hedgehog sniffs the midnight air
And listens to the night.
He blinks his tiny bead-bright eyes,
For hedgehog's sight is dim,
Yet ears and nose will keep him safe
When peril looms most grim.
Tonight he'll walk his lonely paths,
Those ancient woodland lines,
A scuffling, snuffling wanderer
With silver moon-tipped spines.

Margaret Ingall

A TOWN BY NIGHT

SOMETIMES upon my way to sleep,
   when minutes mock and hours creep
and shadowed vistas lithely leap
to thwart the spell of slumber sweet,
I rise with languor, outward bound
where magic, deep and dark, is found.

Here beneath the new moon's reign,
a queen aglow with fine champagne,
commanding stars to entertain
her dusky courts with silver flame,
I wander through the silent streets
lit by slanting, spangled sheets.

There is no-one with whom to speak
and my companion, fickle sleep,
has long since fled on nimble feet,
but upper skies bow down to greet
and guide me on a dreamy flight
across a starstruck town at night.

Rachel Wallace-Oberle

MOUNTAINS

SUCH brow of rock, huge and foreboding,
indulging skyward, solid and old.

Such terrain of solitude, edged by stars,
lit by sunshine, with countenance bold.

Such spirit eternal, silent and peaceful,
the presence of rock held in beauty and time.

Such simple enchantment, power and wonder,
with views to the distance, romantic, sublime.

Mike Fuller

PEARS

I THINK of that house in early evening
Somewhere at the end of Summer

All the doors and windows open
Filled with the afterglow of sun

And the whole house heavy with the scent of pears.
There in the lawn that ancient tree

A hundred Summers old, and maybe more,
Around it a deep, dark ring of pears.

I picked them hour after long hour
To thud into baskets in high hills —

Leaving only the broken ones,
All drizzled and wandering with wasps,

And it was as if the house became some strange ship
I was filling for a long voyage

That the rest of our lives might be made of pears.

Kenneth C. Steven

ONCE UPON A STARRY NIGHT

BENEATH the arching dome of night,
anointed with a starry light,
I wandered with an upward look
and more by instinct than by sight,
a winding little footpath took.
The wind refused to stir the air;
it, too, was breathless, gazing there
at islands hung above the trees,
trailing silver flowers fair,
piercing through the idle leaves.
Oh, my soul is drenched in stars!
They spill from Heaven's crystal jars,
and with their diamonds on display
silently exclaim they are
more beautiful than break of day.

Rachel Wallace-Oberle

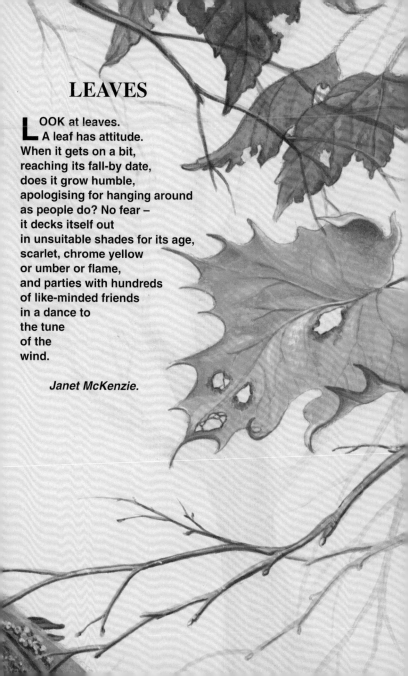

LEAVES

LOOK at leaves.
A leaf has attitude.
When it gets on a bit,
reaching its fall-by date,
does it grow humble,
apologising for hanging around
as people do? No fear –
it decks itself out
in unsuitable shades for its age,
scarlet, chrome yellow
or umber or flame,
and parties with hundreds
of like-minded friends
in a dance to
the tune
of the
wind.

Janet McKenzie.

LOST PROPERTY

Erased from map and memory,
A simple dwelling
Here once stood,
Now, where I stand,
New pasture beds its floor
And lichen patches
LIne the memory
Of a wall.
Like a scarf mislaid,
Then found again
In the undergrowth,
One damp Winter,
It waits for its owner's return,
To claim governance,
Redeem the past.

David Elder

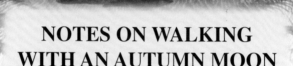

NOTES ON WALKING
WITH AN AUTUMN MOON

WALKING late one violet night
 as Autumn tipped each leaf with light
and gave a sigh of fragrant spice,
I saw a heavy gilded slice
of moon descending as in flight.
Emerging from a sylvan shield,
it followed me across the field,
and eagerly with jewelled intent
pursued me shining as I went
through the countryside revealed.
The moon ignored coquettish stars
that fell to charm him near and far,
and left behind his distant berth
to set before me on the earth
an endless golden boulevard.

Rachel Wallace-Oberle

SUNDAY STEAM

STUTTERING
  under a trellised bridge,
forsaking camera and camcorder,
she heads assertively
Up the Irwell Valley.
At a gated crossing
motorists pay patient deference.
"Leander", queen of the day.
We're in Ramsbottom
For Sunday steam.

Hot dogs with onions,
mustard or relish;
burgers in baps,
black puddings from Bury;
steaming potatoes
in brown paper bags.
A mobile kitchen,
licensed to grill.

A sweet-seller
with cherry lips;
rock of crystal,
of coltsfoot and mint;
Winter candy and ginger
to temper the inrush of air
on this cold
East Lancashire day.

Don Robinson

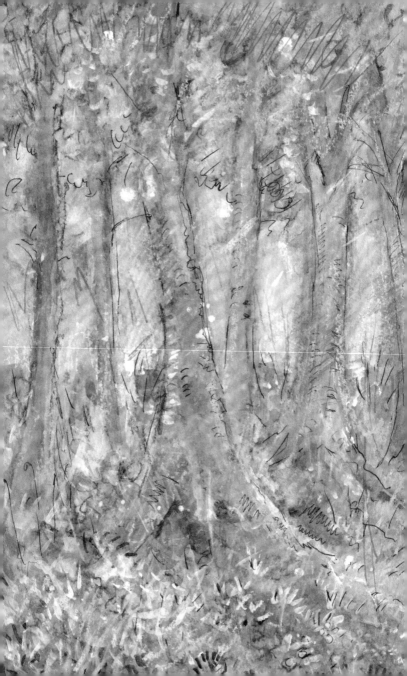

AUTUMN MUSIC

A RHAPSODY of burning gold
Adorns the Autumn trees,
When misty days and fruitfulness
Paint splendour in the leaves.

A serenade of mellow blue
Transforms the Summer skies,
Autumn pastels, golden hues,
The old year slowly dies.

And drying into radiant gold
The countryside rejoices —
For everywhere the Autumn world
Sings out with golden voices.

Peter Cardwell

CARRISTON WATER

IN September's unexpected twilight,
a family of herons
take off with a screech
and languidly,
with steadily pulsing wings,
scan the square mile of a farmland
pimpled with bales of hay.

And in twenty minutes of walking,
the fringes of the reservoir
and the pantiled roofs of Star village
have been doused from a polished sheen
to solemn shade, while the sunset
now begs to be photographed
in its coal effect fireglow.

Ian Nimmo White

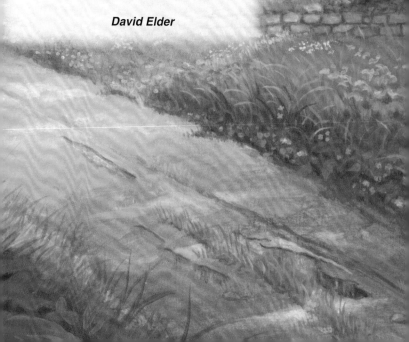

SHATTERED PRIDE

FORTY years on and still I stop,
Crouch down by woodland path,
And place my palm
On Autumn's husks
Of spiky green.

Through the eyes of a child
I squeeze the casings, unravel the seeds
From vacuumed chamber
And feel the conkers
Of playground feuds.

I see them hang by shivering
Slither of plumb-line string,
Waiting for the next hurricane hit
That this time may leave me nothing
But shattered pride.

David Elder

SUDDENLY . . .

NOW cold the winds
In Autumn blow,
With mists that shroud
The lamplight's glow.
Leaves of saffron,
Leaves of brown,
From the Heavens
Flutter down,
To carpet woodland,
Dale and dell,
Where sleepy little
Creatures dwell.
Held high the branches
Of each tree,
In gnarled and tangled
Filigree,
And when dark clouds
Are hanging low,
Precursor to the
Coming snow,
Dame Winter with
Her icy grip
Takes hold to make us
Slide and slip . . .
Then there comes
A great surprise,
And azure blue
Become the skies,
Little birds
Begin to sing,
And suddenly you find
It's Spring!

Brian H. Gent

GREY DUSK

UPON that grey-grained post, a stumpy shape,
 Above the hoar-grey, frost-encrusted grass.
The world outside the speeding train
Was darkening hard and harsh,
But I could sense as that grey owl so slowly
Swivelled head, a dove-soft warmth
Defying, defeating any cold or dark.

Alice Elder

WINTER'S SNOW . . .

HUSHED is the landscape 'neath the snow,
the trees as statues quietly wait;
their sculptured branches silhouettes
in timeless, frosted crystal state,
while snow white webs of garlands' grace,
now whipped by sharpened winds, raw keen,
send flurries of their laden boughs
in feathered drifts upon the scene.
Though this, the first of Winter's snows
there may be more upon the way;
for watch the flakes now settling down —
preparing for a lengthy stay?

Elizabeth Gozney

GOLDCREST

HE wasn't backward
In coming forward,
Greeting us at the end
Of a long line of larch,
Inviting us to enter
His Lilliput kingdom,
The orange glow of his crest
Warming this wintry day.

David Elder

WINTER'S GATE

TIME to pause and contemplate,
 As now we stand at Winter's gate,
The leaves have spiralled from the trees,
Responding to the stiffened breeze,
Hawthorn berries glisten red
And hips abound in flower bed,
Soon the earth will turn to steel
And water droplets will congeal,
To sugar wood and path and lane,
Confirming Winter's here again,
And so the icy grip will cling,
Till snowdrops cast their spell in Spring.

Brian H. Gent

A WINTER AFTERNOON

A WINTER afternoon, but quiet and grey,
The stocky figure limped along the road,
His dog ahead, around, on pounding legs
That felt no jar from friendly ground.
But he, for whom each step
Was hard-won hostage in a losing fight,
Was whistling like a bird.

The gallant sound transformed
That Winter afternoon.

Alice Elder

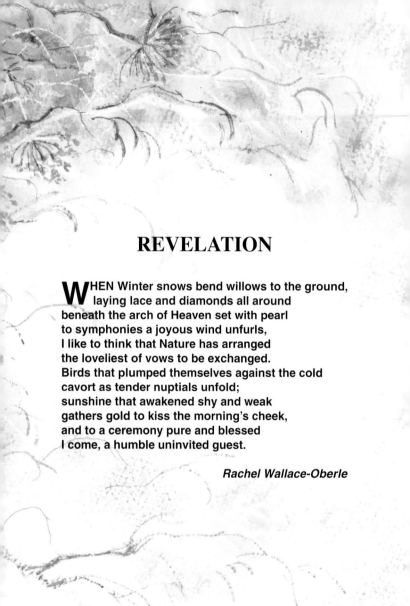

REVELATION

WHEN Winter snows bend willows to the ground,
laying lace and diamonds all around
beneath the arch of Heaven set with pearl
to symphonies a joyous wind unfurls,
I like to think that Nature has arranged
the loveliest of vows to be exchanged.
Birds that plumped themselves against the cold
cavort as tender nuptials unfold;
sunshine that awakened shy and weak
gathers gold to kiss the morning's cheek,
and to a ceremony pure and blessed
I come, a humble uninvited guest.

Rachel Wallace-Oberle

STARS

I LOOKED into the sky tonight
and saw a host of white
companions lying undiscovered
in a hollow field. Gathered
like nocturnal mushrooms, they
appeared quite inexplicably
from some unfathomable root
imbedded in the sky. What
jewel day might discover
with which to blind or cover,
they will be there, the stars, ten
thousand in the sky, but hidden.

John Ellis

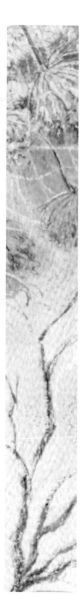

The artists are:-

Matt Bain; At The Wood's Edge.
Jackie Cartwright; Redbreast,
Apple Tree Dreams,
Sweet Scent Of Twilight, Grey Dusk.
Henri Damoiseaux; A Summer Day.
John Dugan; A Cat Called Tea Bag,
Harbour Scene, Like A Picture Book,
Caterpillars, Notes On Walking With An
Autumn Moon.
Eunice Harvey; Nature's Child,
Woodlarks, Sweet William, Peacock,
Pears, Winter's Gate.
Harry McGregor; To A Spring Wind,
Where Minnows Swim,
Peaceful Rendezvous, Carriston Water.
Norma Maclean; Flame, A Day In April,
Sea Change, Speaking Volumes,
A Town By Night, A Winter Afternoon.
Keith Robson; Lost Property.
Ruth M. L. Walker; Autumn Music.
Joseph Watson; Garden Party,
The Cuckoo, Midnight Traveller, Leaves,
Shattered Pride, Goldcrest.
Staff Artists; Green, Urbanised,
The Horse On The Hill, Summer Lightning,
Harebell, Summer's Music Hall,
Briar Roses On The Path,
Glowing Seascape, Summer Healing,
Nature's Paradise, Mountains, Once Upon
A Starry Night, Sunday Steam, Suddenly,
Winter's Snow, Revelation, Stars.